Baby Animals

CONTENTS

WHO ARE WE?

All animals reproduce: that is they produce young. This is important as it prevents the species from dying out and becoming extinct.

Parents and Young

Most female animals produce young. It is only in very rare cases, such as the seahorse, that the male produces the young. Most mammals have a breeding season, a mating season and a gestation period, before they give birth. The breeding and mating season refers to the time when the male and female mammals come together in order to produce a baby. The gestation period is the time in which the young develops inside the female before it is born. Mammals have different gestation periods, ranging from a few weeks, to a few months, and even as long as a year!

Baby animals are known by different names. An elephant's baby, for example, is known as a calf

The baby kangaroo, or joey, climbs into its mother's pouch right after it is born and stays there till it is strong enough to face the outside world!

Loving Care

All animals have different ways of caring for their young. Some care for their offspring with a similar devotion to how our parents look after and care for us. But there are some species, like the giant water bug and the stickleback fish, among whom the father takes on the full responsibility of looking after the eggs and the young. Among others, such as emperor penguins, the male partner takes on the responsibility of looking after their young, while the female partner hunts for food. But, later, both parents raise the chick. In certain animals, the young are also looked after by other members of the pack.

The father emperor penguin hatches the egg and takes care of the chick until the mother returns from hunting

Being Born

Most young ones are either born as babies or hatch out from eggs. Mammals give birth to babies, while reptiles, amphibians, birds and fish lay eggs. However, certain creatures, like snakes, reproduce in three ways: most species of snakes lay eggs, from which the young are born; some species give birth to baby snakes; in certain species of snakes, such as the viper, the eggs grow and hatch inside the mother snake and then the live young are born.

YOUNG CATS

Big cats have unique ways of looking after their young. Since they are born in the wild, the cubs of big cats are well protected and trained to survive an attack from other predators.

The mother carries her cubs in her mouth, usually holding them by the neck

Baby Cats

Adult female tigers usually give birth to two to four cubs every two and a half years. This gives the mother tigers enough time to raise their cubs and ensures that each one is independent before they give birth again. Tiger cubs are born on a cushion of grass inside a cave or in the middle of dense vegetation. The cubs are nursed for an average of three to six months and are looked after only by the mother. The mother moves the cubs by carrying them in her mouth, from one hiding place to another, to avoid predators like hyenas, jackals and leopards.

CREATURE PROFILE

Common Name:	Tiger
Scientific name:	*Panthera Tigris*
Found in:	South-East Asia, China and Russia
Weight:	1–1.3 kilograms (kg) (2–3 pounds (lbs))
Feed on:	First 6–8 weeks: Mother's milk After 6–18 weeks: Prey killed by the mother After 18 weeks: Prey hunted by themselves

Cheetah cubs grow rapidly. They begin to see after they are four days old and grow teeth when they are three weeks old!

Young Spots

Female cheetahs may give birth to as many as nine cubs at a time! The cubs, born blind and helpless, weigh between 150-300 grams (g) (5-10 ounces (oz)) at birth. Cheetah cubs are born with spots on the body. They also have fur on their necks. This fur, called the mantle, helps the cub camouflage itself. The fur slowly sheds as the baby grows. The mother cheetah hides the cubs in tree tops to protect them from predators like lions and hyenas.

A Happy Family

Lions live in groups known as prides and all females of a single pride give birth at the same time. This helps them to share responsibility and look after all the cubs at the same time. The cubs live exclusively on their mother's milk for about two months, after which she will lead them to feed on an animal that she has killed. When they are a little older the mother leads prey to her cubs to teach them to hunt by themselves.

Cubs chase one another, wrestle and fight playfully - practising some of the skills they will need in their adult life

PACK THEM UP

Creatures like the wolf and fox follow seasonal routines, breeding once during the year. Hyenas, however, do not follow any seasonal pattern and breed any time of the year.

Young Kits

Adult male and female red foxes pair for life. Red foxes have a gestation period of nearly two months. Just before and after giving birth, the female fox does not leave her den. It is the male fox who provides her with food during this period. The female gives birth to a litter of four to thirteen kits at a time. Kits are born blind and begin to see after 10-14 days. The kits leave the den after four weeks but continue to feed on their mother's milk for about eight-ten weeks.

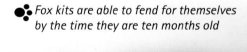 *Fox kits are able to fend for themselves by the time they are ten months old*

CREATURE PROFILE

Common Name:	Red fox
Scientific name:	*Vulpes Vulpes*
Found in:	United States and Canada
Colour:	Sandy brown coat at birth
Weight:	50–150 g (1.7–5.2 oz)
Feed on:	Milk, small insects and rodents

Group Care

Wolf pups are born blind and deaf. They are nursed by their mother for three weeks in the den. During this time the mother licks them clean and even swallows their excretions to keep the den clean and hygienic! The pups begin to see in two weeks and make short trips outside the den when they are four weeks old. They also begin eating meat during this time, although they are weaned only after eight weeks.

Spotted hyena cubs are moved to a communal den at two-six weeks of age

The mother wolf's milk has antibodies that make the pups stronger, so she encourages them to suckle till they are two months old

Fittest Survives

The newborns of spotted hyenas weigh between 1-1.6 kg (2.2-3.6 lbs) and are born with their eyes open and with teeth as well. Because the dominant cub will receive more food and grow faster, the cubs start fighting among themselves soon after birth – often resulting in the death of the weaker ones. The cubs feed on their mother's milk, which is rich in protein and fat, until they are 14-18 months old.

BIG BABIES

Bigger animals like elephants, hippos and rhinos have unique ways of giving birth and looking after their young. Even when they are newborn, these baby animals are huge when compared with other baby animals.

Elephants and Calves

The female elephant has the longest gestation period among animals — 22 months! She generally bears one calf at a time. The calf learns to stand on its own feet within just 30 minutes of its birth. Since female elephants live in packs, it helps mothers to select other female elephants as babysitters, who help to raise and care for their calves. The newborn calf suckles many times in a single day, drinking almost 11 litres (3 gallons) of milk!

The nutritious milk helps the calf grow very fast: it gains 1 kg (2 lbs) of weight every day!

CREATURE PROFILE

Common Name:	Elephant
Scientific name:	*Elephantidae*
Found in:	Asia and Africa
Weight:	90–115 kg (158–253 lbs)
Feed on:	Up to 2 years: Mother's milk

Born Underwater

Female hippos give birth to a single calf at a time. Hippos are one of the few mammals that give birth underwater. The newborn calf immediately swims to the surface to breathe. The calf also suckles milk underwater. However, when the water is too deep, the calf rests its head or rides on its mother's back. Because hippos are herd animals, hippo calves of the same herd generally play together. The mothers also leave their calves with other females of their herd to babysit them.

Fighting for Birth

Male rhinos fight with one another to win the right to mate with the females. After mating the male rhino leaves, leaving the female rhino to give birth and raise the calf by herself. A single calf is born after a gestation period of about 18 months. The calf is well protected by its mother. It is nursed for almost a year, though it starts eating vegetation a few weeks after birth. It stays with its mother till she reproduces again after a few years. The calf, now grown, leaves the mother and goes its own way.

Hippo calves weigh 27-45 kg (60-100 lbs) and measure up to 1 m (3 ft) long!

The rhino mother builds a strong bond with her calf when she nurses it

HOOVED ANIMALS

Animals like giraffes, zebras and wildebeest, that have a hard covering on their feet, are called hooved animals. These animals use their hooves to walk and run.

Tall Babies

Female giraffes have a long gestation period of 15 months. The giraffes give birth while standing up. So newborn giraffe calves begin their lives by falling 1.8 m (6 ft) to the ground! The calves are born in calving grounds and the female giraffe returns to the same breeding ground year-after-year to give birth. The females go off to feed everyday, leaving the young calves to protect one another. While adult giraffes are rarely attacked by predators, the young often fall prey to lions, leopards and hyenas. When the calves grow a little older they accompany their mothers to forage in the wild, though they continue to drink their mother's milk till they are 15 months old.

Giraffe calves are born with horns that lie flat against their heads. They pop up when they are a week old!

CREATURE PROFILE

Common Name:	Giraffe
Scientific name:	*Giraffa Camelopardalis*
Found in:	Africa
Height:	1.8 m (6 ft)
Weight:	68 kg (150 lbs)
Feed on:	Milk and young shoots and leaves

Knowing Your Own

Zebras start to mate at three years of age and have a gestation period lasting for a whole year. Zebra foals are very well developed at birth and can move with the herd within an hour of their birth. The foals can even run short distances within 45 minutes! Mothers keep their newborn calves away from all the other zebras for two to three days. This way the newborns soon recognise their mother by sight, sound and smell. The calves are brown and white in colour when they are born and develop black and white stripes as they grow older.

Born Together

The breeding time of the entire herd of wildebeest is synchronised – so around 400,000 calves are born at the same time! The calves can run within minutes of their birth and in three days the calves are strong enough to move with the herd. This helps them protect themselves against predators like lions, hyenas, cheetahs and leopards. Calves suckle for at least six months, although they begin grazing with the herd at about 10 days old.

The stripes on zebra calves help to camouflage them, making it difficult for predators to distinguish the calves from the adults

Within days of their birth, wildebeest calves can run fast enough to keep up with the herd

LITTLE ANTLERS

The deer family includes a large number of species, including the antelope and the moose. They are distinguished by their antlers.

The young deer can stand within minutes of its birth and can walk after just a few hours. It stays close to its mother who is very aggressive in defending her young against predators

The Young and the Old

The male member of the deer family grows antlers. For the young bucks, the first pair of antlers grow from bumps on their head that they have from birth. The antlers are wrapped in a velvety layer and stay that way for several months. Once the bone in the antlers becomes hard, the velvet is torn away. Most young are born with white spots on their fur, which they lose as they grow older. Fawns are licked clean by their mother, until they are free of any kind of smell, to avoid being detected by predators.

Blackbuck Kids

Female blackbuck antelope have a gestation period of about five months and give birth to two fawns in a year, each approximately six months apart. The young feed on their mother's milk for about two weeks, after which they are ready to join the herd. But the calves are quite helpless and dependent on their parents and members of the herd for their safety. When they are six months old, the young males join male groups. The females, however, stay with their mother until they are a year old.

CREATURE PROFILE

Common Name:	Elk
Scientific name:	*Alces Americanus*
Found in:	Forests in Northern Hemisphere ranging from temperate to sub-Arctic climate
Colour:	Reddish brown coat
Weight:	14 kg (31 lbs) at birth; 113 kg (250 lbs) by six months
Feed on:	Mother's milk and plants

The young elk spends the first few weeks in hiding with its mothers to avoid being spotted by predators

The mother blackbuck suckles her young every two-three hours in the first few days

Born to be Big

The mother elk gives birth to a single calf after a gestation of about 250 days. Feeding on its mother's nutritious milk the calf gains weight rapidly — about 1 kg (2.2 lbs) everyday! By six months of age it weighs five times as much as when it was born! The calf is spotted at birth. Its loses its spots as it grows. It is also odourless, which is important as it prevents predators from smelling its presence. The mother and calf use many vocalisations to keep track of each other. The mother mews and whines, while the calf bleats when in distress. The calf is protected by its mother for a year until she is ready to reproduce again.

BABY APES AND MONKEYS

Apes and monkeys care for their young with a lot of attention. Since the mother does not reproduce frequently she is able to give a lot of time to her offspring.

Shy Young

Female gorillas have a slow reproductive cycle. They might give birth to only two to six offspring in 40-50 years of their life. There is no fixed mating season and the female gorillas reproduce after a gestation period of eight months. They typically bear one infant every six-eight years. A newborn gorilla weighs about 1.8 kg (4 lbs). It spends its first few months with its mother and starts to walk only at four-five months of age. Although the baby drinks milk until three years of age, it starts on solid food at eight months old.

The mother gorilla spends a lot of time playing with and grooming her baby

CREATURE PROFILE

Common Name:	Mountain gorilla
Scientific name:	*Gorilla Beringei Beringei*
Found in:	Central Africa
Weight:	1.8 kg (4 lbs)
Feed on:	Milk and plants

Chimp Babies

The chimpanzee has black hair on its body, but the baby chimp also has a white tuft of hair on the rump. The newborn stays close to the mother, hugging her for shelter and warmth. The mother also makes bowl-shaped nests out of leaves for her baby to sleep in at night. The baby chimp is quite playful and learns a lot of skills that it needs as an adult, such as using tools, climbing and wrestling. Since the chimpanzee uses sounds and gestures to communicate, the young chimp is taught to follow them.

Young chimps are weaned at three years of age but they remain close to their mothers till they are about 10 years old

Monkey Tale

Most baby monkeys are cared for in a similar way. They suckle milk within an hour of being born. For the first few months infants cling to their mother's underbelly as she walks. At about three to five months of age they begin riding on their mother's back till they are old enough to move about on their own. The mothers also spend a lot of time grooming their babies to keep them free of lice and ticks. Baby monkeys learn tricks like climbing trees and swinging on branches by watching their mothers do it.

See how the infant Bolivian squirrel monkey is clinging to its mother's back

POUCH BABIES

Marsupials are mammals in which the female has a pouch called the marsupium. It is in this pouch that the babies of these animals feed and grow.

Joey, Joey

A baby kangaroo is called a joey. Like all other marsupials, baby kangaroos are born after a very short gestation period of just 31–36 days. The forelimbs are developed in a newborn joey and allow it to creep into its mother's pouch as soon as it is born. The joey stays in the mother's pouch until it is about nine months old. Once it starts to mature and grow hair, the joey slowly starts to detach itself from its mother and leaves the pouch looking for food.

Pink Jellybean

A koala baby is also called a joey. The koala joey is also born after a short gestation period of 35 days. The newborn koala looks like a pink jellybean! It is blind and has no hair or ears. The koala has a pouch that it can tighten with the help of muscles. So once the baby koala is born, the mother tightens its pouch to prevent the baby from falling. The joey lives on its mother's milk for the first 22 weeks and grows hair, ears and eyes during that time. From 22–30 weeks it is fed on pap, a substance that is produced by the mother, in addition to milk.

As it grows, the joey make short trips outside its mother's pouch but gets back in at the slightest sign of danger!

Baby Bilby

A female bilby has a backward facing pouch. She gives birth to two-three infants after a gestation period of just 21 days! The bilby mother is equipped to carry two or three young in her pouch at one time. The young animals suckle in the pouch for 70-80 days, after which they are released in the burrow by their mother.

The backward facing pouch of the bilby helps to keep the infants safe when the mother digs the ground to burrow or look for food

At five months the baby koala comes out of its mother's pouch to explore but goes right back in when it feels threatened. When it is eight months old it leaves its mother's pouch forever

CREATURE PROFILE

Common Name:	Koala
Scientific Name:	*Phascolarctos Cinereuss*
Found in:	Eastern coast of Australia from Adelaide to southern part of Cape York Peninsula
Weight:	Less than 1gm (0.0022 lbs)!
Length:	2 cm (0.78 in)
Colour:	Pink, with no hair, eyes or ears
Feed on:	First 22 weeks: Mother's milk 22–30 weeks: Pap, a substance produced by the mother

YOUNG FLIERS

All species of birds in the world lay eggs, covered with a hard shell that helps to protect the young growing within. These are usually then incubated by the birds in order to hatch them.

The Nest is Home

Many birds make nests to lay eggs in. Nests are made in areas difficult to spot by predators. Some nests are simple, while some are very intricate. The weaver bird, for example, knots and weaves strands of paddy, leaves and twigs to make flask shaped nests. The African palm swift uses its own saliva to stick its down-and-feather nest to the underside of a palm leaf. The eggs are also stuck to the nest to prevent them from falling out.

Chick Care

Some chicks can be helpless when they hatch, while some are independent. Some chicks are born small and blind without feathers and need their parents to care for them and feed them - the chicks of herons, owls and woodpeckers for example. Some chicks, such as those of chickens and ducks, are born with good eyesight. They are covered with feathers and have a strongly built skeleton, making them capable of taking care of themselves shortly after they hatch and leaving the nest soon after.

Male weaver birds make up to 500 trips when collecting twigs to make the nest!

Chicks are able to feed on their own only after they fledge or learn to fly. Until then it is the parents who feed them regurgitated food

CREATURE PROFILE

Common Name:	Ostrich
Scientific name:	*Struthio Camelus*
Found in:	Africa
Weight:	Eggs: 1.4 kg (3 lbs)
	Chicks: 45 kg (110 lbs) after one year
Length:	Eggs: 15 cm (6 in) long and 13 cm (5 in) wide
	Chicks: 25 cm (10 in) during the first year
Colour:	Eggs: Shiny white
	Chicks: Greyish brown and white
Feed on:	Seeds and plants

Ostriches make very good parents. They take good care of their chicks till they are able to fend for themselves

Large Chicks

Ostriches make good parents. Their eggs are incubated by the male at night and the female during the day. This is because the dark feathers of the male ostrich make it invisible at night and the light feathers of the female blend in with the natural surroundings during the day. The chicks emerge after 45 days. Although they can run within minutes of hatching, they are followed around and fed by their parents for the first year.

SMALL SLITHERS

Most reptiles lay eggs from which the young hatch: they are known as oviparous creatures. Some, however, give birth to live young and are known as viviparous animals. Some reptiles keep the eggs inside their body until they are about to hatch: they are known as ovoviviparous.

Caring Parents?

Snakes do not make the best parents because they abandon their eggs soon after they lay them. But this is their way of ensuring that they are not tempted to eat up their own hatchlings! Few snakes actually brood their eggs. Egg layers usually leave their eggs in a burrow, in holes, under logs, or any other place that will be well hidden. King cobras, however, make elaborate nests with leaves. The female then lays the eggs and incubates them. The male guards the nesting area fiercely. However, both the parents leave just before the eggs are about to hatch to avoid eating the babies.

It is possible for more than one baby snake to pop out of a single egg!

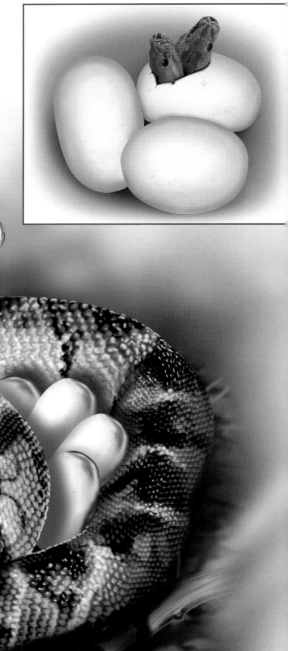

The bush viper does not eat for days when it incubates its eggs

The female python coils around the eggs and incubates them by shivering!

Baby Snakes

Baby snakes may look quite different from their parents: the rattlesnake, for example, is born without a rattle. It starts forming its rattle only after it begins shedding its skin. Most baby snakes begin to get the colouration of their parents gradually, increasing with each layer of skin they shed. Baby snakes are not as aggressive as their parents. Venomous baby snakes carry the same type of venom as their parents. But since they have smaller fangs their bite is not as dangerous.

Young Bites

The female crocodile lays about 50-80 eggs at one time at a spot hidden from predators. Depending on the species, the mother may or may not incubate the eggs, but she guards the nest till the eggs hatch. The warmth of the soil and vegetation helps to incubate the eggs. When they are ready to hatch out, the baby crocodiles make a yapping sound from inside the eggs to signal to their mother. The mother then digs the eggs out of the nest. The crocklets use their egg-tooth to bite their way out of the shell. Sometimes the mother also gently squeezes the eggs inside her mouth to release the crocklets. Unlike other reptiles, the female crocodile does not abandon her eggs or hatchlings: in fact, she protects the young ones from predators. They even get into their mother's mouth or climb on to her back while she swims!

Crocklets are looked after by their mothers for about a year

CREATURE PROFILE

Common Name:	American crocodile
Scientific Name:	*Crocodylus Acutus*
Found in:	Throughout Central America and Mexico and parts of South America
Length:	20 cm (8 in)
Colour:	Greenish-grey with black cross bands
Feed on:	Water insects and shellfish

HOW SMALL CAN IT GET?

Most insects lay hundreds of eggs at a time. Indeed, there are more insects in the world than all the animals added together. Some female insects are quite amazing — they can reproduce without their eggs being fertilised by the male!

A Bug's Life

Insects pass through four distinct phases in their lives — egg, larva or nymph, pupa and adult. The egg develops over a period of time and grows into the larva or the nymph. The larva goes through several stages. It sheds its skin at every stage, which is known as moulting. Some insects grow into adults straight from a larva while others transform into a pupa and develop a hard outer shell acting as a protective cover for the growing insect inside. The insect breaks out of the pupa when fully grown.

Being Beautiful

Like most other insects butterfly eggs also pass through stages before becoming colourful butterflies. Butterfly eggs have a hard outer shell and are fixed to leaves with special glue made by the butterfly. After a few weeks the eggs grow into caterpillars. Caterpillars are multi-legged creatures and spend all their time searching for food. After about two weeks caterpillars turn into a chrysalis. The adult butterfly emerges out of the chrysalis and is known as imago.

 The illustration shows the life cycle of the mosquito

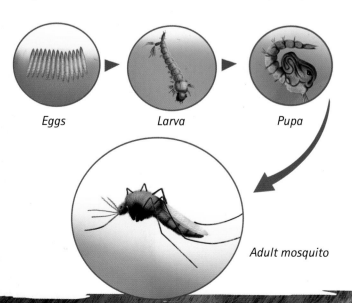

Eggs   *Larva*   *Pupa*

Adult mosquito

The butterfly emerges from the chrysalis, which becomes transparent a few days before the adult butterfly emerges

The Queen's Court

A bee colony consists of one breeding female called the queen, a few thousand males known as drones, and many more female bee workers. Eggs are laid in a wax honeycomb and the larva is fed with a royal jelly, produced by the worker bees, and pollen from flowers. From the many larva, the worker bees select a special few who are put on an exclusive royal jelly diet so that they grow to become queen bees later.

The queen larvae develop in special queen cells, which are larger than the other cells

BABIES IN SNOW

Animals in Arctic and Antarctic regions display unique characteristics in reproducing and looking after their young. The young are well protected against the cold and are soon taught to fend for themselves.

Snowy Den

Female polar bears prepare a den for their babies at one end of a tunnel. Then they seal the opening with soft snow to keep the den snug. The female bears give birth, usually to two cubs, between the end of November and early January. The cubs are born blind and are covered with fluffy white hair. This makes them look like snowballs! The cubs feed on their mother's milk, which has more fat in it than the milk of other bears. This helps insulate them against the cold.

The polar bear cubs stay with their mother for two and a half years, during which she protects them and teaches them to hunt

CREATURE PROFILE

Common Name:	Polar bear
Scientific name:	*Ursus Maritimus*
Found in:	Greenland, Norway, Canada, USA, Russia and Arctic sea pack ice
Weight:	450–900 g (16–31 oz)
Feed on:	Up to 2 years: Mothers milk

Out in the World

Around April, when it is a little less cold outside, the cubs make their first trip out of the den to see the world outside! The mother takes them out on a journey to the sea to hunt and feed. Along the way the mother digs resting pits in the snow to provide shelter to the cubs from the freezing wind. The cubs rest and feed in these pits. They also watch their mother hunt animals, such as seals, and this helps them learn the art of hunting too.

Mother polar bears are very protective of their cubs, risking their own lives if necessary!

Hairy Calves

The female musk ox gives birth during summer. The calf is born with a thick curly coat. However, the coat cannot always save the calf from the biting cold so it snuggles under its mother's long woolly coat for warmth. The calf feeds on its mother's milk for the first three months, after which it begins eating grass. Musk ox are herd animals and adult members of a herd defend the calves of the herd together.

Musk oxen form an outward facing circle around the calves to protect the calves from animals such as the Arctic fox

GROWING UP IN THE COLD

Polar animals such as penguins and seals breed and reproduce in the freezing climate. The babies are well adapted to survive the cold. They usually huddle close to one another to keep warm.

The emperor chicks have extra down under their feathers that helps to keep them warm

Emperor Father

Emperor penguins are the only birds that breed in the freezing Antarctic winter. The female emperor penguin lays only one egg, which she rolls to the male, who immediately puts it in his brood pouch to keep it warm. The female heads for the sea, leaving the male to hatch the egg and care for the chick. The male emperor penguins huddle in groups called turtles to keep the eggs warm. These responsible fathers neither eat nor move while incubating the egg!

CREATURE PROFILE

Common Name:	Emperor penguin
Scientific name:	*Aptenodytes Forsteri*
Found in:	Antarctica
Colour:	Covered with light gray and white down feathers
Weight:	450 g (16 oz)
Feed on:	Regurgitated food of parents

JAN-MAR
Feeding

60-100 mile
march to rookery
APR

Adults
leave;
Chicks
fledge;
DEC

Females
go off to feed

Mating
MAY

Males go to feed;
Cycle repeat
6 more times

Females return

Males incubate eggs
JUN-JUL

Hatching
AUG

Feeding chicks
SEP-OCT

Chicks form groups
to stay warm
OCT-NOV

The image shows the feeding habits of the emperor penguins, their breeding cycle and the raising of the emperor chicks

Chick Care

The father emperor penguin's work does not end when the egg hatches. Now he has to feed and care for the chick. He feeds it with a milky substance produced by him till the mother returns from the sea. When the mother returns the parents raise the chick together, feeding them regurgitated food. All the chicks of a flock form a creche to remain safe and warm when their parents are out fishing. Parents call out aloud to their chicks as they return. The chicks recognise and return their parent's call.

The mother's fat-rich milk helps the pup to grow big and get lots of blubber to keep warm

Seal Pups

The harp seal pup is born on ice. The soft and silky white coat helps it to blend in with the snow and remain undetected by its predators. It is nursed for about 12 days. A harp seal pup's teeth will grow only if it eats so it is weaned quickly. As it grows the young harp seal moves from land to the sea and learns to swim.

WATER BABIES

Creatures living underwater have many ways of reproducing and taking care of their young ones. Sea mammals suckle their young while baby fish mainly feed on vegetation in the sea.

Strange Fish

Most fish live and reproduce in the same water. But there are some, like salmon, that live in the salty water of the sea but reproduce in fresh water. Salmon die soon after they spawn and the eggs hatch by themselves. The larvae travel hundreds of miles all by themselves to the sea! American eels live in fresh water but travel to the sea to spawn. The eggs hatch and swim by themselves back up the same river their parent came from!

Sea Mammals

Female sea mammals like whales and dolphins give birth to live young that they nourish with their milk. The young ones can swim at, or soon after, their birth. They suckle their mother's milk right after birth. The high fat content in the mother's milk helps the calves gain weight rapidly. Depending on the species, calves are weaned for between four-eleven months. They swim close to their mother for about a year during which they learn how to survive.

The adult salmon faces a lot of danger when it travels to its spawning grounds

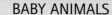

The baby whale swims close to its mother and is carried in its mother's slip stream

Eggs and More

Sharks reproduce in one of three different ways. While some sharks give birth to live young, some are known to lay eggs that hatch and release the young. There is also a third type that hatch the egg inside the body and then give birth. The newborn sharks, called pups, are born with a full set of teeth and can take care of themselves immediately.

CREATURE PROFILE

Common Name:	Blue whale
Scientific name:	*Balaenoptera musculus*
Breed in:	Temperate and tropical waters
Weight:	2,200–2,700 kg (5,000–6,000 lbs)!
Length:	7 m (23 ft) at birth!
Feed on:	Mother's milk and smaller sea creatures

Shark pups quickly swim away from their mother after birth so that they are not eaten by her!

FROGS AND TURTLES

Several water creatures, such as the frog and the turtle, have unique ways of breeding and rearing their young.

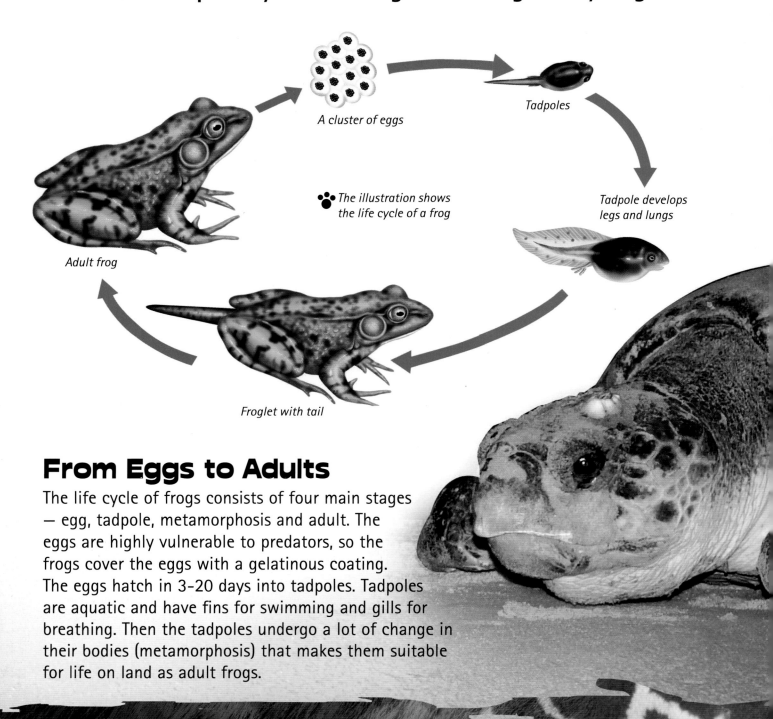

A cluster of eggs

Tadpoles

The illustration shows the life cycle of a frog

Tadpole develops legs and lungs

Adult frog

Froglet with tail

From Eggs to Adults

The life cycle of frogs consists of four main stages — egg, tadpole, metamorphosis and adult. The eggs are highly vulnerable to predators, so the frogs cover the eggs with a gelatinous coating. The eggs hatch in 3-20 days into tadpoles. Tadpoles are aquatic and have fins for swimming and gills for breathing. Then the tadpoles undergo a lot of change in their bodies (metamorphosis) that makes them suitable for life on land as adult frogs.

Baby Care

Frogs return to the original pond where they were hatched to spawn their young ones. Frogs often carry their young ones on their back or their hind legs to protect them from predators. The male Australian pouched frog has pouches along its body in which the tadpoles are kept till they metamorphosise into froglets. The female gastric brooding frog is known to swallow its tadpoles and then develop them in her stomach! Some frogs also hide the tadpoles in their vocal sacs till they are fully developed.

Water and Sand

Marine turtles are found offshore and near coastlines. But they swim long distances to lay and hatch their eggs on the beach. Females leave the ocean at night to lay their eggs in the sand. Baby turtles hatch a month or two after the eggs are laid. The baby turtles use an egg-tooth to peck their way out of the egg shell. This egg-tooth is only used for this purpose and is lost soon after the eggs hatch. The baby turtles hatch during the day but only return to the ocean after it is dark to avoid predators.

The mother turtle lays her eggs in the sand and then leaves. The heat of the sand incubates the eggs, out of which the babies emerge

CREATURE PROFILE

Common Name:	Green sea turtle
Scientific name:	*Chelonia mydas*
Found in:	Atlantic, Eastern Pacific Ocean
Length:	20–25 cm (8–10 in)
Feed on:	Worms, insects, grass, algae

MUM OR DAD

In most species of animals it is the female who produces the young. With seahorses, however, it is the male who does so! There are also some species of fish in which the male partner rears and cares for the young.

Loyal Partners

The seahorse is the only animal species where the male reproduces instead of the female! Most seahorses live with single partner all their life, although some species are known to mate with more than one individual. The partners greet each other in the morning with various body movements. After this, they go their separate ways — looking for food the whole day.

The male stickleback fish guards the eggs and, as the eggs need plenty of oxygen to develop, he also directs waves of oxygen-filled water towards them with his fins!

Male seahorses show off their pouches during mating to impress females

Father's Child

Seahorse reproduction occurs between May and August. The female lays 250-600 eggs inside the male's brood sack - a pouch to keep the eggs in. After depositing the eggs, the female goes away, leaving the male to look after the eggs. In certain species, the female may deposit her eggs inside more than one male before her eggs are finished. The male seahorse lays the eggs after a gestation period of 40 to 50 days.

Daddy's Care

While for most animal species the reproduction of, and care for, the young is the responsibility of the mother, there are a few species of animals among which the male parent looks after the young. The giant water bug is a good example. The female bug latches on to the back of the male and deposits eggs on his back. The male bug carries this load for one full month, not eating during this time, for fear of eating up the eggs. Similarly, the male stickleback fish has the job of protecting fertilised eggs. The male fish uses secretions from its kidneys to glue together bits of vegetation to build a nest. After the female lays the eggs, the male fertilises them and flattens them into sheets at the bottom of the nest. It inspects the eggs constantly and eats any egg that may be rotten. Once the fry hatch out the male fish protects them for a week by gathering them in its mouth from the water and returning them to the nest.

The male seahorse's pouch closes with the eggs safely inside. When the father is ready to deliver, the pouch opens and tiny seahorses pop out!

CREATURE PROFILE

Common Name:	Seahorse
Scientific name:	*Hippocampus Denise*
Found in:	Western Atlantic Ocean and Indo-Pacific region
Length:	70-120 cm (27-47 in)
Feed on:	Fish, small shrimps and crabs

AT THE FARM

Looking after farms animals like cows, sheep and pigs requires a lot of skill and care. While the mother looks after her young, it is also the responsibility of the farmer to provide some elements of care.

Farm owners avoid milking the cows for about three months after their calves are born so that the calf gets its share of the mother's nutritious milk

Cows and Calves

The calf can stand within 45 minutes of its birth. It begins sucking its mother's milk after two-three hours. The first milk of the mother cow, called the colostrum, is filled with antibodies and minerals essential for the newborn calf's health. The mother licks her calf to stimulate breathing, blood circulation and excretion, as well as to form a bond. The calf usually follows its mother in the first few weeks of its birth. But as it grows older, it tends to roam and graze with other calves.

Lamb Breeding

Sheep are bred in various parts of the world for meat, wool and even milk. The female sheep (the ewe) can produce offspring until about 15 years of age. The gestation period of ewes is four to five months. Sheep are seasonal breeders and the lambs are generally born between spring and summer. With the weather being warmer and the abundance of fresh grass, this is the best time for their birth. The mothers lick their young ones and, like cows, produce colostrum that helps the lambs grow stronger. The lambs are weaned when they are three-four weeks old.

🐾 *After they are weaned, lambs feed on grass and other vegetation*

Horsing Around

Mature female horses, also known as mares, have a gestation period of about 11 months. Domestic mares are given special care to ensure that the young foals are healthy. Vaccinations are also provided to keep them free of any disease. Once a foal is born, the mare licks it to keep it clean and also to improve blood circulation. Foals usually stand up and feed on their mother's milk within an hour of their birth. A foal begins to eat hay, grain and grass when it is about four weeks old but continues to feed on its mother's milk until four-eight months of age.

🐾 *The foal and the mare are usually kept away from other horses right after birth but can join the herd within a few weeks*

A month after their birth, puppies become active and playful. Indeed, they can sometimes be quite mischievous!

AT HOME

Most of us love having pets like dogs and cats at home. It is not only important to care for them, but also to know how to care for the health of pups or kittens if they have them.

Puppy Love

Puppies are born with their eyes and ears closed. They open their eyes and ears about two weeks after they are born. Newborn puppies feed on colostrum as soon as they are born. Puppies start teething when they are three to seven weeks old. The mother dog does not leave the puppy alone until it is four weeks old. In the first few weeks puppies sleep a lot, which helps them grow.

Growing Up

In the first two weeks the pup only crawls to get close to its mother. It makes a whining noise most of the time and its tiny limbs will twitch occasionally. At three weeks the pup will let out soft barks and also start moving around. It begins to play and wrestle with its siblings too. As the days pass its activities increase - as does the noise it makes! The pup is considered an adult when it is one year old.

Pups begin to look like their parents as they grow. Pups of long-haired dogs will slowly grow similarly long hair

Newborn kittens wriggle under their mother's belly, each competing for a teat at which to suckle milk

Cat Talk

The gestation period of a cat lasts for 60 to 63 days, after which she gives birth to a litter of four-six kittens. The kittens are born blind and deaf. The mother curls her body around her young in order to keep them warm and safe. She also defends her kittens aggressively. The young feed on their mother's milk every one-two hours. This helps them to double their weight in a week. Like dog pups, kittens also spend most of their time sleeping. Only after two weeks, when they begin to see and hear, do they start moving about. They feed on solid food when they are about three-four weeks old, although they are not completely weaned until seven-eight weeks of age.

PHYSICAL DIFFERENCE

Many baby animals resemble their parents – they just look like smaller versions of them. A baby dog or a baby elephant can be easily recognised, for example.

However, there are many animals that look completely different from their parents. The larva of a butterfly, or a tadpole, for example, leaves you guessing what they could grow up to be! They undergo massive change to become like their parents.

Glossary

Abandon: To leave something and go away

Aggressively: Fiercely

Amphibians: Creatures that can live both in water and on land

Antibodies: Useful chemicals that prevent diseases

Antlers: Branched horns on the head of members of the deer family

Blubber: Fat

Camouflage: To blend in with the surrounding

Communicate: To interact with one another

Distress: To be in trouble

Detach: To move away from someone

Extinct: To exist no more

Forage: Search for food

Gestures: To move a part of the body in order to express something

Grazing: Feeding on grass in a field

Huddle: To come close together

Hygienic: Clean and free of infection

Incubate: To keep eggs warm to hatch them

Independent: Not depending on anyone else for food or shelter

Keep track: To keep watch

Moult: To shed old skin and develop new skin

Pollen: Yellow powdery substance found on flowers

Predators: Animals that hunt and eat other animals

Regurgitate: To bring semi-digested food back to the mouth

Snuggle: To cuddle for warmth

Suckle: To have the mother's milk

Synchronised: To happen at the same time

Teething: To grow teeth

Vaccination: Injections given to prevent some deadly diseases

Vocalisations: Calls or sounds made from mouth

Wean: To stop having milk

Wrestling: Grappling with another

Index

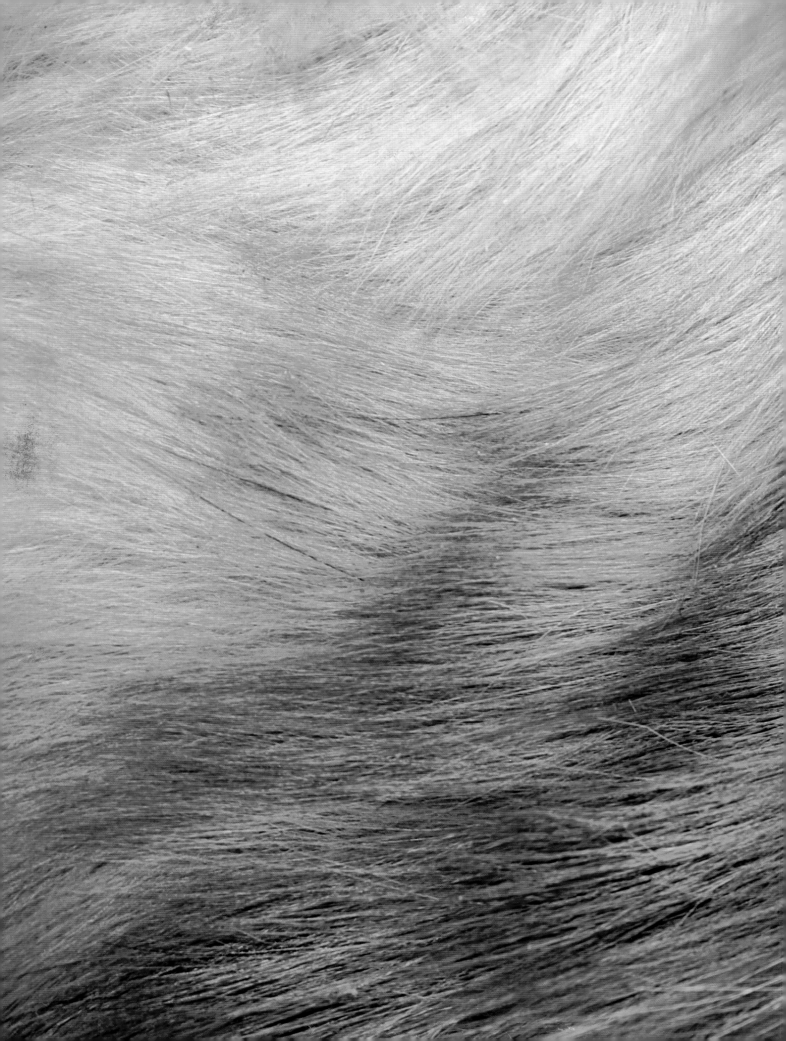